A Little Fish Book about
RUTH

Illustrated by Gordon Stowell

Ruth and Orpah lived with their mother-in-law Naomi. The three women had a hard time finding enough food to eat.

"Let's each go to our relatives and friends so they can help us," Naomi said.

But Naomi's relatives lived in Bethlehem. This was many miles away in another country.

Orpah went back to live with her relatives.

But Ruth did not want to leave Naomi all alone.

Ruth said to Naomi,
"Where you go, I will go; where you stay, I will stay. Your people shall be my people, and your God, my God."

So Ruth and Naomi went off together to find food in Bethlehem. They arrived just at harvest time.

Naomi said to Ruth, "People who have no food can go to the grain fields. If there is any grain left lying on the ground, they can take it."

So early each morning Ruth went to a grain field owned by Boaz.

"Who is that girl?" Boaz asked his helper. "Her name is Ruth," the helper said. "She comes to pick up grain. She shares it with her mother Naomi."

Boaz said, "Be kind to Ruth. Leave a little extra grain where she will find it to fill her basket."

And Boaz told the helpers to share their water and lunch with Ruth, too.

Every day Ruth picked up grain in Boaz' fields until the harvest was over. One day Boaz asked Ruth to marry him.

Ruth and Boaz asked Naomi to come to live with them. Ruth and Boaz had a baby boy. This family thanked God for His loving care.

This story can be found in the Bible in the book of Ruth.

Little Fish Books

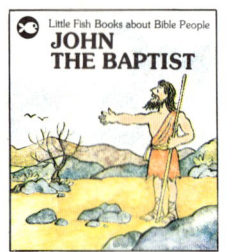